This Journal Belongs to

....

Created by Arielle Haughee

ORANGE BLOSSOM
PUBLISHING

Maitland, Florida

Published 2021 by Orange Blossom Publishing
Maitland, Florida
www.orangeblossombooks.com

ISBN: 978-1-949935-19-6

A Note from Arielle

You have a creative calling to fulfill. It can be completely energizing and also entirely draining. But your work is important. Art shares a universal truth we all recognize. It moves people and gives vividness to the human experience.

The creative journey is never an easy one, and you need to trust the process. Follow your instincts when something doesn't seem quite right. Take the time to mold your work until you feel its ready. But also push yourself. Be stubborn about achieving your goals but also be forgiving when you need to.

Your biggest enemy to creative achievement will be yourself. Self-criticism can be crippling and excuses will constantly seek you out.

Another big block? Shiny new ideas. They tempt us away from our current projects and lie to us, saying they will be easier and better. Use the pages at the end of this journal to write down ideas as they hit so you can leave them there and continue on your current goals. Once finished, you can come back to them.

I wish you many, many productive days where you are fully tapped into your creative potential. Keep up the important work!

Stay Connected to Your WHY

Why do you take on your creative endeavor? What part of the process brings you the most joy? You will need to come back to this when you are frustrated or buried in self-doubt, wondering why you even bother.

Create an Inspiration Board

You may be working on one large project or several smaller ones, either way you can create an inspiration board for one or more works. You can do this online using a site like Pinterest or a physical board you glue things to. Use the prompts below to help you think of what to include.

Colors..

....

....

Visuals...

....

....

Smells..

....

....

Food..

....

....

Music...

....

....

Sounds...

....

....

Textures...

....

....

Patterns...

....

....

Light..

....

....

 # Quote Keeper

Quotes are a great way to help you understand you aren't alone in your journey and many people face the same challenges you do. Whenever you come across a quote that strikes a cord with you, write it down here.

....
....
....
....
....
....
....
....
....
....
....
....
....
....
....
....
....
....
....
....
....
....
....
....
....
....

# Quote Keeper

This is my favorite writing quote about your first efforts: "I'm writing a first draft and reminding myself that I'm simply shoveling sand into a box so that later I can build castles." -Shannon Hale

Prioritizing Your Time

The activities on the following pages will help you determine your goals and the best times to work on them.

My big goal(s) for the year: ....
....
....
....
....
....
....

After you write your big goals, go back and label your goals in order of importance. *1 = most important to me, 2 = medium importance, 3 = least important of my goals.*

Next, write actionable steps to achieve your goal, something you could do each week to make progress toward your big goal.

Big goal: ....
Actionable Steps: ....
....
....

Big goal: ....
Actionable Steps: ....
....
....

Big goal: ....
Actionable Steps: ....
....
....

Big goal: ....
Actionable Steps: ....
....
....

Prioritizing Your Time

Times in my schedule I am available to work on my creative projects:

Monday:	
Tuesday:	
Wednesday:	
Thursday:	
Friday:	
Saturday:	
Sunday:	

Now think about times when you are the most focused (morning, afternoon, night?).
Go back to the chart you filled out above and number each one of your available work
times to show how focused and productive you are at that time.
1 = most productive time, 2 = average productive time, 3 = least productive

****The goals labeled 1 in importance on the left page should get
your number 1 focus time on the right page!****

Week 1

Inspiration

Focus word or phrase

I will use the outdoors to keep me inspired by

I will use music or art to keep me inspired by

What I'm reading

I want to emulate

Other creatives I will talk to this week

When I feel frustrated, I will

I won't give up when

Planned break

I will be brave when

I will be proud when

I will share my work on

Productivity

Big goal(s) for this week:

Priority Level (1-3):

....

....

....

Week 1

Monday:	Actionable tasks:	When I Will Complete:	Completed?:

Tuesday:	Actionable tasks:	When I Will Complete:	Completed?:

Wednesday:	Actionable tasks:	When I Will Complete:	Completed?:

Thursday:	Actionable tasks:	When I Will Complete:	Completed?:

Friday:	Actionable tasks:	When I Will Complete:	Completed?:

Weekend:	Actionable tasks:	When I Will Complete:	Completed?:

For next week: ....

....

....

....

Week 2

Inspiration

Focus word or phrase

I will use the outdoors to keep me inspired by

I will use music or art to keep me inspired by

What I'm reading

I want to emulate

Other creatives I will talk to this week

When I feel frustrated, I will

I won't give up when

Planned break

I will be brave when

I will be proud when

I will share my work on

Productivity

Big goal(s) for this week: **Priority Level (1-3):**

....

....

....

Week 2

Monday:	Actionable tasks:	When I Will Complete:	Completed?:
Tuesday:	Actionable tasks:	When I Will Complete:	Completed?:
Wednesday:	Actionable tasks:	When I Will Complete:	Completed?:
Thursday:	Actionable tasks:	When I Will Complete:	Completed?:
Friday:	Actionable tasks:	When I Will Complete:	Completed?:
Weekend:	Actionable tasks:	When I Will Complete:	Completed?:

For next week: ....

....

....

....

Week 3

Inspiration

Focus word or phrase

I will use the outdoors to keep me inspired by

I will use music or art to keep me inspired by

What I'm reading

I want to emulate

Other creatives I will talk to this week

When I feel frustrated, I will

I won't give up when

Planned break

I will be brave when

I will be proud when

I will share my work on

Productivity

Week 3

Big goal(s) for this week: Priority Level (1-3):

....

....

....

	Actionable tasks:	When I Will Complete:	Completed?:
Monday:			
Tuesday:			
Wednesday:			
Thursday:			
Friday:			
Weekend:			

For next week: ....

....

....

....

Week 4

Inspiration

Focus word or phrase

I will use the outdoors to keep me inspired by

I will use music or art to keep me inspired by

What I'm reading

I want to emulate

Other creatives I will talk to this week

When I feel frustrated, I will

I won't give up when

Planned break

I will be brave when

I will be proud when

I will share my work on

Productivity

Big goal(s) for this week: Priority Level (1-3):

....

....

....

Monday:	Actionable tasks:	When I Will Complete:	Completed?:

Tuesday:	Actionable tasks:	When I Will Complete:	Completed?:

Wednesday:	Actionable tasks:	When I Will Complete:	Completed?:

Thursday:	Actionable tasks:	When I Will Complete:	Completed?:

Friday:	Actionable tasks:	When I Will Complete:	Completed?:

Weekend:	Actionable tasks:	When I Will Complete:	Completed?:

For next week: ....

....

....

....

Monthly Reflections

1. Would you consider this month successful? Why or why not?

2. When were you at your best? Why do you think that is?

3. When were you at your least productive? Why?

4. Is there anything you are being too hard on yourself about?

5. What can you do next month to consider yourself successful?

....

....

....

....

....

....

....

....

....

....

....

....

....

....

....

....

....

....

....

....

....

Warm Up Activities

Creativity is like a faucet, you have to turn the water on first and let it run before it gets warm. As some writers say, "BIC," which stands for "Butt in Chair." Don't wait for inspiration or your muse to hit, plan a time to work each day and get started. Brainstorm ideas to warm up your juices. For writers, it may be timed quick writes, artists may do quick sketches, photographers can take some shots to visualize their compositions. Brainstorm activities you can do to get your flow going.

....

....

....

....

....

....

....

....

....

....

....

....

....

....

....

....

....

....

....

....

....

....

Week 5

Inspiration

Focus word or phrase

I will use the outdoors to keep me inspired by

I will use music or art to keep me inspired by

What I'm reading

I want to emulate

Other creatives I will talk to this week

When I feel frustrated, I will

I won't give up when

Planned break

I will be brave when

I will be proud when

I will share my work on

Productivity

Big goal(s) for this week:

Priority Level (1-3):

....

....

....

Week
5

	Actionable tasks:	When I Will Complete:	Completed?:
Monday:			
Tuesday:			
Wednesday:			
Thursday:			
Friday:			
Weekend:			

For next week: ....

....

....

....

Week 6

Inspiration

Focus word or phrase

I will use the outdoors to keep me inspired by

I will use music or art to keep me inspired by

What I'm reading

I want to emulate

Other creatives I will talk to this week

When I feel frustrated, I will

I won't give up when

Planned break

I will be brave when

I will be proud when

I will share my work on

Productivity

Big goal(s) for this week: Priority Level (1-3):

....

....

....

Week 6

Monday:	Actionable tasks:	When I Will Complete:	Completed?:

Tuesday:	Actionable tasks:	When I Will Complete:	Completed?:

Wednesday:	Actionable tasks:	When I Will Complete:	Completed?:

Thursday:	Actionable tasks:	When I Will Complete:	Completed?:

Friday:	Actionable tasks:	When I Will Complete:	Completed?:

Weekend:	Actionable tasks:	When I Will Complete:	Completed?:

For next week: ....

....

....

....

Week 7

Inspiration

Focus word or phrase

I will use the outdoors to keep me inspired by

I will use music or art to keep me inspired by

What I'm reading

I want to emulate

Other creatives I will talk to this week

When I feel frustrated, I will

I won't give up when

Planned break

I will be brave when

I will be proud when

I will share my work on

Productivity

Big goal(s) for this week:

Priority Level (1-3):

....
....
....

Week 7

	Actionable tasks:	When I Will Complete:	Completed?:
Monday:			
Tuesday:			
Wednesday:			
Thursday:			
Friday:			
Weekend:			

For next week: ....
....
....
....

Inspiration

Week 8

Focus word or phrase

I will use the outdoors to keep me inspired by

I will use music or art to keep me inspired by

What I'm reading

I want to emulate

Other creatives I will talk to this week

When I feel frustrated, I will

I won't give up when

Planned break

I will be brave when

I will be proud when

I will share my work on

Productivity

Big goal(s) for this week:

Priority Level (1-3):

....

....

....

Week 8

Monday:	Actionable tasks:	When I Will Complete:	Completed?:

Tuesday:	Actionable tasks:	When I Will Complete:	Completed?:

Wednesday:	Actionable tasks:	When I Will Complete:	Completed?:

Thursday:	Actionable tasks:	When I Will Complete:	Completed?:

Friday:	Actionable tasks:	When I Will Complete:	Completed?:

Weekend:	Actionable tasks:	When I Will Complete:	Completed?:

For next week: ....

....

....

....

Monthly Reflections

1. Would you consider this month successful? Why or why not?

2. When were you at your best? Why do you think that is?

3. When were you at your least productive? Why?

4. Is there anything you are being too hard on yourself about?

5. What can you do next month to consider yourself successful?

Addressing Bad Habits

We all have them. Spend some time thinking about what your particular bad habits are, what causes them, and what you can do to redirect yourself in a more positive or productive way.

Bad Habit	When It Occurs	Why It Happens	Better Alternative

Week 9

Inspiration

Focus word or phrase

I will use the outdoors to keep me inspired by

I will use music or art to keep me inspired by

What I'm reading

I want to emulate

Other creatives I will talk to this week

When I feel frustrated, I will

I won't give up when

Planned break

I will be brave when

I will be proud when

I will share my work on

Productivity

Big goal(s) for this week: Priority Level (1-3):

....

....

....

Week 9

	Actionable tasks:	When I Will Complete:	Completed?:
Monday:			
Tuesday:			
Wednesday:			
Thursday:			
Friday:			
Weekend:			

For next week: ....

....

....

....

Week 10

Inspiration

Focus word or phrase

I will use the outdoors to keep me inspired by

I will use music or art to keep me inspired by

What I'm reading

I want to emulate

Other creatives I will talk to this week

When I feel frustrated, I will

I won't give up when

Planned break

I will be brave when

I will be proud when

I will share my work on

Productivity

Big goal(s) for this week:

Priority Level (1-3):

....

....

....

Week 10

Day	Actionable tasks:	When I Will Complete:	Completed?:
Monday:			
Tuesday:			
Wednesday:			
Thursday:			
Friday:			
Weekend:			

For next week: ....

....

....

....

Week 11

Inspiration

Focus word or phrase

I will use the outdoors to keep me inspired by

I will use music or art to keep me inspired by

What I'm reading

I want to emulate

Other creatives I will talk to this week

When I feel frustrated, I will

I won't give up when

Planned break

I will be brave when

I will be proud when

I will share my work on

Productivity

Big goal(s) for this week:

Priority Level (1-3):

....

....

....

Week 11

	Actionable tasks:	When I Will Complete:	Completed?:
Monday:			
Tuesday:			
Wednesday:			
Thursday:			
Friday:			
Weekend:			

For next week: ....

....

....

....

Week 12

Inspiration

Focus word or phrase

I will use the outdoors to keep me inspired by

I will use music or art to keep me inspired by

What I'm reading

I want to emulate

Other creatives I will talk to this week

When I feel frustrated, I will

I won't give up when

Planned break

I will be brave when

I will be proud when

I will share my work on

Productivity

Big goal(s) for this week: Priority Level (1-3):

....

....

....

	Actionable tasks:	When I Will Complete:	Completed?:
Monday:			
Tuesday:			
Wednesday:			
Thursday:			
Friday:			
Weekend:			

For next week: ....

....

....

....

Monthly Reflections

1. Would you consider this month successful? Why or why not?

2. When were you at your best? Why do you think that is?

3. When were you at your least productive? Why?

4. Is there anything you are being too hard on yourself about?

5. What can you do next month to consider yourself successful?

Switch It Up

We often get into patterns with where and when we work. Think about changing your routine a bit for the next month and see how it impacts your creativity and flow.

New locations to try ....
....
....
....
....
....

New times to squeeze in some creative work ....
....
....
....
....
....

New tools or technology to try ....
....
....
....
....
....

Ideas to organize or update my work space ....
....
....
....
....

Other ideas ....
....
....
....

Week 13

Inspiration

Focus word or phrase

I will use the outdoors to keep me inspired by

I will use music or art to keep me inspired by

What I'm reading

I want to emulate

Other creatives I will talk to this week

When I feel frustrated, I will

I won't give up when

Planned break

I will be brave when

I will be proud when

I will share my work on

Productivity

Big goal(s) for this week: Priority Level (1-3):

....

....

....

Week 13

Monday:	Actionable tasks:	When I Will Complete:	Completed?:

Tuesday:	Actionable tasks:	When I Will Complete:	Completed?:

Wednesday:	Actionable tasks:	When I Will Complete:	Completed?:

Thursday:	Actionable tasks:	When I Will Complete:	Completed?:

Friday:	Actionable tasks:	When I Will Complete:	Completed?:

Weekend:	Actionable tasks:	When I Will Complete:	Completed?:

For next week: ....

....

....

....

Week
14

Inspiration

Focus word or phrase

I will use the outdoors
to keep me inspired by

I will use music or art
to keep me inspired by

What I'm reading

I want to emulate

Other creatives I will
talk to this week

When I feel frustrated,
I will

I won't give up when

Planned break

I will be brave when

I will be proud when

I will share my work on

Productivity

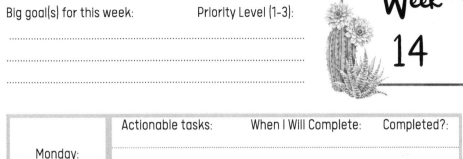

Big goal(s) for this week: Priority Level (1-3):

....
....
....

Week 14

	Actionable tasks:	When I Will Complete:	Completed?:
Monday:			
Tuesday:			
Wednesday:			
Thursday:			
Friday:			
Weekend:			

For next week: ....
....
....
....

Week

15

Inspiration

Focus word or phrase

I will use the outdoors to keep me inspired by

I will use music or art to keep me inspired by

What I'm reading

I want to emulate

Other creatives I will talk to this week

When I feel frustrated, I will

I won't give up when

Planned break

I will be brave when

I will be proud when

I will share my work on

Productivity

Big goal(s) for this week: Priority Level (1-3):

....

....

....

Week 15

	Actionable tasks:	When I Will Complete:	Completed?:
Monday:			
Tuesday:			
Wednesday:			
Thursday:			
Friday:			
Weekend:			

For next week: ....

....

....

....

Week
16

Inspiration

Focus word or phrase

I will use the outdoors to keep me inspired by

I will use music or art to keep me inspired by

What I'm reading

I want to emulate

Other creatives I will talk to this week

When I feel frustrated, I will

I won't give up when

Planned break

I will be brave when

I will be proud when

I will share my work on

Productivity

Big goal(s) for this week: Priority Level (1-3):

....
....
....

Week 16

	Actionable tasks:	When I Will Complete:	Completed?:
Monday:			
Tuesday:			
Wednesday:			
Thursday:			
Friday:			
Weekend:			

For next week: ....
....
....
....

Monthly Reflections

1. Would you consider this month successful? Why or why not?

2. When were you at your best? Why do you think that is?

3. When were you at your least productive? Why?

4. Is there anything you are being too hard on yourself about?

5. What can you do next month to consider yourself successful?

My Accomplishments

Too often we focus on the things we didn't do or that didn't work out for us. Use the space on this page to record what you have done, large and small, throughout the year. Congratulate yourself on your progress and your journey.

....

....

....

....

....

....

....

....

....

....

....

....

....

....

....

....

....

....

....

....

....

....

....

....

....

....

....

....

Week 17

Inspiration

Focus word or phrase

I will use the outdoors to keep me inspired by

I will use music or art to keep me inspired by

What I'm reading

I want to emulate

Other creatives I will talk to this week

When I feel frustrated, I will

I won't give up when

Planned break

I will be brave when

I will be proud when

I will share my work on

Productivity

Big goal(s) for this week: Priority Level (1-3):

....

....

....

	Actionable tasks:	When I Will Complete:	Completed?:
Monday:			
Tuesday:			
Wednesday:			
Thursday:			
Friday:			
Weekend:			

For next week: ....

....

....

....

Week 18

Inspiration

Focus word or phrase

I will use the outdoors to keep me inspired by

I will use music or art to keep me inspired by

What I'm reading

I want to emulate

Other creatives I will talk to this week

When I feel frustrated, I will

I won't give up when

Planned break

I will be brave when

I will be proud when

I will share my work on

Productivity

Big goal(s) for this week: Priority Level (1-3):

....

....

....

Week 18

	Actionable tasks:	When I Will Complete:	Completed?:
Monday:			
Tuesday:			
Wednesday:			
Thursday:			
Friday:			
Weekend:			

For next week: ....

....

....

....

Week 19

Inspiration

Focus word or phrase

I will use the outdoors to keep me inspired by

I will use music or art to keep me inspired by

What I'm reading

I want to emulate

Other creatives I will talk to this week

When I feel frustrated, I will

I won't give up when

Planned break

I will be brave when

I will be proud when

I will share my work on

Productivity

Big goal(s) for this week: Priority Level (1-3):

....

....

....

Week 19

	Actionable tasks:	When I Will Complete:	Completed?:
Monday:			
Tuesday:			
Wednesday:			
Thursday:			
Friday:			
Weekend:			

For next week: ....

....

....

....

Week 20

Inspiration

Focus word or phrase

I will use the outdoors to keep me inspired by

I will use music or art to keep me inspired by

What I'm reading

I want to emulate

Other creatives I will talk to this week

When I feel frustrated, I will

I won't give up when

Planned break

I will be brave when

I will be proud when

I will share my work on

Productivity

Big goal(s) for this week: **Priority Level (1-3):**

Week 20

....

....

....

Monday:	Actionable tasks:	When I Will Complete:	Completed?:

Tuesday:	Actionable tasks:	When I Will Complete:	Completed?:

Wednesday:	Actionable tasks:	When I Will Complete:	Completed?:

Thursday:	Actionable tasks:	When I Will Complete:	Completed?:

Friday:	Actionable tasks:	When I Will Complete:	Completed?:

Weekend:	Actionable tasks:	When I Will Complete:	Completed?:

For next week: ....

....

....

....

Monthly Reflections

1. Would you consider this month successful? Why or why not?

2. When were you at your best? Why do you think that is?

3. When were you at your least productive? Why?

4. Is there anything you are being too hard on yourself about?

5. What can you do next month to consider yourself successful?

....

....

....

....

....

....

....

....

....

....

....

....

....

....

....

....

....

....

....

....

....

....

....

A Letter to Yourself

Creativity and its driving force take place in the mind. Self-criticism and the feeling of failure can be crippling to the creative process. Write a letter of encouragement to yourself for when you feel like quitting. Remember to read it when you feel low.

....

....

....

....

....

....

....

....

....

....

....

....

....

....

....

....

....

....

....

....

....

....

....

....

Week 21

Inspiration

Focus word or phrase

I will use the outdoors to keep me inspired by

I will use music or art to keep me inspired by

What I'm reading

I want to emulate

Other creatives I will talk to this week

When I feel frustrated, I will

I won't give up when

Planned break

I will be brave when

I will be proud when

I will share my work on

Productivity

Big goal(s) for this week: Priority Level (1-3):

....

....

....

Week 21

	Actionable tasks:	When I Will Complete:	Completed?:
Monday:			
Tuesday:			
Wednesday:			
Thursday:			
Friday:			
Weekend:			

For next week: ....

....

....

....

Week 22

Inspiration

Focus word or phrase

I will use the outdoors to keep me inspired by

I will use music or art to keep me inspired by

What I'm reading

I want to emulate

Other creatives I will talk to this week

When I feel frustrated, I will

I won't give up when

Planned break

I will be brave when

I will be proud when

I will share my work on

Productivity

Big goal(s) for this week: **Priority Level (1-3):**

....

....

....

	Actionable tasks:	When I Will Complete:	Completed?:
Monday:			
Tuesday:			
Wednesday:			
Thursday:			
Friday:			
Weekend:			

For next week: ....

....

....

....

Week 23

Inspiration

Focus word or phrase

I will use the outdoors to keep me inspired by

I will use music or art to keep me inspired by

What I'm reading

I want to emulate

Other creatives I will talk to this week

When I feel frustrated, I will

I won't give up when

Planned break

I will be brave when

I will be proud when

I will share my work on

Productivity

Big goal(s) for this week: Priority Level (1-3):

....

....

....

Monday:	Actionable tasks:	When I Will Complete:	Completed?:

Tuesday:	Actionable tasks:	When I Will Complete:	Completed?:

Wednesday:	Actionable tasks:	When I Will Complete:	Completed?:

Thursday:	Actionable tasks:	When I Will Complete:	Completed?:

Friday:	Actionable tasks:	When I Will Complete:	Completed?:

Weekend:	Actionable tasks:	When I Will Complete:	Completed?:

For next week: ....

....

....

....

Week 24

Inspiration

Focus word or phrase

I will use the outdoors to keep me inspired by

I will use music or art to keep me inspired by

What I'm reading

I want to emulate

Other creatives I will talk to this week

When I feel frustrated, I will

I won't give up when

Planned break

I will be brave when

I will be proud when

I will share my work on

Productivity

Big goal(s) for this week: Priority Level (1-3):

....

....

....

Week 24

	Actionable tasks:	When I Will Complete:	Completed?:
Monday:			
Tuesday:			
Wednesday:			
Thursday:			
Friday:			
Weekend:			

For next week: ....

....

....

....

Monthly Reflections

1. Would you consider this month successful? Why or why not?

2. When were you at your best? Why do you think that is?

3. When were you at your least productive? Why?

4. Is there anything you are being too hard on yourself about?

5. What can you do next month to consider yourself successful?

....

....

....

....

....

....

....

....

....

....

....

....

....

....

....

....

....

....

....

....

....

....

Mid-Year Schedule Re-evaluation

Your schedule may have changed at this point, or you've realized parts of your plan aren't working out. Look at your schedule again and see what adjustments you may need. Fill out the new schedule below with when you can work on your projects.

What worked well that I want to keep: ....

....

What needs to change: ....

....

....

Monday:	
Tuesday:	
Wednesday:	
Thursday:	
Friday:	
Saturday:	
Sunday:	

Week 25

Inspiration

Focus word or phrase

I will use the outdoors to keep me inspired by

I will use music or art to keep me inspired by

What I'm reading

I want to emulate

Other creatives I will talk to this week

When I feel frustrated, I will

I won't give up when

Planned break

I will be brave when

I will be proud when

I will share my work on

Productivity

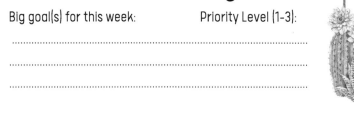

Big goal(s) for this week: Priority Level (1-3):

....

....

....

Week 25

	Actionable tasks:	When I Will Complete:	Completed?:
Monday:			
Tuesday:			
Wednesday:			
Thursday:			
Friday:			
Weekend:			

For next week: ....

....

....

....

Week 26

Inspiration

Focus word or phrase

I will use the outdoors to keep me inspired by

I will use music or art to keep me inspired by

What I'm reading

I want to emulate

Other creatives I will talk to this week

When I feel frustrated, I will

I won't give up when

Planned break

I will be brave when

I will be proud when

I will share my work on

Productivity

Big goal(s) for this week: Priority Level (1-3):

....

....

....

Monday:	Actionable tasks:	When I Will Complete:	Completed?:

Tuesday:	Actionable tasks:	When I Will Complete:	Completed?:

Wednesday:	Actionable tasks:	When I Will Complete:	Completed?:

Thursday:	Actionable tasks:	When I Will Complete:	Completed?:

Friday:	Actionable tasks:	When I Will Complete:	Completed?:

Weekend:	Actionable tasks:	When I Will Complete:	Completed?:

For next week: ....

....

....

....

Week 27

Inspiration

Focus word or phrase

I will use the outdoors to keep me inspired by

I will use music or art to keep me inspired by

What I'm reading

I want to emulate

Other creatives I will talk to this week

When I feel frustrated, I will

I won't give up when

Planned break

I will be brave when

I will be proud when

I will share my work on

Productivity

Week 27

Big goal(s) for this week: Priority Level (1-3):

....

....

....

Monday:	Actionable tasks:	When I Will Complete:	Completed?:

Tuesday:	Actionable tasks:	When I Will Complete:	Completed?:

Wednesday:	Actionable tasks:	When I Will Complete:	Completed?:

Thursday:	Actionable tasks:	When I Will Complete:	Completed?:

Friday:	Actionable tasks:	When I Will Complete:	Completed?:

Weekend:	Actionable tasks:	When I Will Complete:	Completed?:

For next week: ....

....

....

....

Week 28

Inspiration

Focus word or phrase

I will use the outdoors
to keep me inspired by

I will use music or art
to keep me inspired by

What I'm reading

I want to emulate

Other creatives I will
talk to this week

When I feel frustrated,
I will

I won't give up when

Planned break

I will be brave when

I will be proud when

I will share my work on

Productivity

Big goal(s) for this week: Priority Level (1-3):

....

....

....

Week 28

	Actionable tasks:	When I Will Complete:	Completed?:
Monday:			
Tuesday:			
Wednesday:			
Thursday:			
Friday:			
Weekend:			

For next week: ....

....

....

....

Monthly Reflections

1. Would you consider this month successful? Why or why not?

2. When were you at your best? Why do you think that is?

3. When were you at your least productive? Why?

4. Is there anything you are being too hard on yourself about?

5. What can you do next month to consider yourself successful?

....
....
....
....
....
....
....
....
....
....
....
....
....
....
....
....
....
....
....
....
....
....

Harnessing Your Senses

Utilizing your senses to incorporate into your art can give it powerful dimension, whether they are part of the inspiration or woven into the tapestry of your craft. Reflect on the connection between your art and sensory elements.

Sight ....

....

....

....

....

Sound..

....

....

....

....

Flavor..

....

....

....

....

Touch..

....

....

....

....

Scent..

....

....

....

....

Inspiration

Week 29

Focus word or phrase

I will use the outdoors to keep me inspired by

I will use music or art to keep me inspired by

What I'm reading

I want to emulate

Other creatives I will talk to this week

When I feel frustrated, I will

I won't give up when

Planned break

I will be brave when

I will be proud when

I will share my work on

Productivity

Big goal(s) for this week: Priority Level (1-3):

....

....

....

Week 29

	Actionable tasks:	When I Will Complete:	Completed?:
Monday:			
Tuesday:			
Wednesday:			
Thursday:			
Friday:			
Weekend:			

For next week: ....

....

....

....

Week 30

Inspiration

Focus word or phrase

I will use the outdoors to keep me inspired by

I will use music or art to keep me inspired by

What I'm reading

I want to emulate

Other creatives I will talk to this week

When I feel frustrated, I will

I won't give up when

Planned break

I will be brave when

I will be proud when

I will share my work on

Productivity

Big goal(s) for this week:

Priority Level (1-3):

....

....

....

Week 30

	Actionable tasks:	When I Will Complete:	Completed?:
Monday:			
Tuesday:			
Wednesday:			
Thursday:			
Friday:			
Weekend:			

For next week: ....

....

....

....

Week 31

Inspiration

Focus word or phrase

I will use the outdoors to keep me inspired by

I will use music or art to keep me inspired by

What I'm reading

I want to emulate

Other creatives I will talk to this week

When I feel frustrated, I will

I won't give up when

Planned break

I will be brave when

I will be proud when

I will share my work on

Productivity

Big goal(s) for this week: Priority Level (1-3):

....

....

....

Week 31

	Actionable tasks:	When I Will Complete:	Completed?:
Monday:			
Tuesday:			
Wednesday:			
Thursday:			
Friday:			
Weekend:			

For next week: ....

....

....

....

Week 32

Inspiration

Focus word or phrase

I will use the outdoors to keep me inspired by

I will use music or art to keep me inspired by

What I'm reading

I want to emulate

Other creatives I will talk to this week

When I feel frustrated, I will

I won't give up when

Planned break

I will be brave when

I will be proud when

I will share my work on

Productivity

Big goal(s) for this week:

Priority Level (1-3):

....

....

....

Week 32

	Actionable tasks:	When I Will Complete:	Completed?:
Monday:			
Tuesday:			
Wednesday:			
Thursday:			
Friday:			
Weekend:			

For next week: ....

....

....

....

Monthly Reflections

1. Would you consider this month successful? Why or why not?
2. When were you at your best? Why do you think that is?
3. When were you at your least productive? Why?
4. Is there anything you are being too hard on yourself about?
5. What can you do next month to consider yourself successful?

....
....
....
....
....
....
....
....
....
....
....
....
....
....
....
....
....
....
....
....
....
....

Recognizing Triggers for Lows

An emotional roller caoster is often part of creating art. Being able to recognize your lows so that you can anticipate them and redirect yourself will help smooth out some of the curving track.

When I Felt Low	Possible Trigger	What Helps Me Feel Better

Week 33

Inspiration

Focus word or phrase

I will use the outdoors to keep me inspired by

I will use music or art to keep me inspired by

What I'm reading

I want to emulate

Other creatives I will talk to this week

When I feel frustrated, I will

I won't give up when

Planned break

I will be brave when

I will be proud when

I will share my work on

Productivity

Week 33

Big goal(s) for this week: Priority Level (1-3):

....

....

....

	Actionable tasks:	When I Will Complete:	Completed?:
Monday:			
Tuesday:			
Wednesday:			
Thursday:			
Friday:			
Weekend:			

For next week: ....

....

....

....

Week 34

Inspiration

Focus word or phrase

I will use the outdoors to keep me inspired by

I will use music or art to keep me inspired by

What I'm reading

I want to emulate

Other creatives I will talk to this week

When I feel frustrated, I will

I won't give up when

Planned break

I will be brave when

I will be proud when

I will share my work on

Productivity

Big goal(s) for this week: Priority Level (1-3):

....

....

....

Week 34

Monday:	Actionable tasks:	When I Will Complete:	Completed?:

Tuesday:	Actionable tasks:	When I Will Complete:	Completed?:

Wednesday:	Actionable tasks:	When I Will Complete:	Completed?:

Thursday:	Actionable tasks:	When I Will Complete:	Completed?:

Friday:	Actionable tasks:	When I Will Complete:	Completed?:

Weekend:	Actionable tasks:	When I Will Complete:	Completed?:

For next week: ....

....

....

....

Week 35

Inspiration

Focus word or phrase

I will use the outdoors to keep me inspired by

I will use music or art to keep me inspired by

What I'm reading

I want to emulate

Other creatives I will talk to this week

When I feel frustrated, I will

I won't give up when

Planned break

I will be brave when

I will be proud when

I will share my work on

Productivity

Big goal(s) for this week:

Priority Level (1-3):

....

....

....

Week 35

	Actionable tasks:	When I Will Complete:	Completed?:
Monday:			
Tuesday:			
Wednesday:			
Thursday:			
Friday:			
Weekend:			

For next week: ....

....

....

....

Week 36

Inspiration

Focus word or phrase

I will use the outdoors to keep me inspired by

I will use music or art to keep me inspired by

What I'm reading

I want to emulate

Other creatives I will talk to this week

When I feel frustrated, I will

I won't give up when

Planned break

I will be brave when

I will be proud when

I will share my work on

Productivity

Big goal(s) for this week:

....

....

....

Priority Level (1-3):

Week 36

	Actionable tasks:	When I Will Complete:	Completed?:
Monday:			
Tuesday:			
Wednesday:			
Thursday:			
Friday:			
Weekend:			

For next week: ....

....

....

....

Monthly Reflections

1. Would you consider this month successful? Why or why not?

2. When were you at your best? Why do you think that is?

3. When were you at your least productive? Why?

4. Is there anything you are being too hard on yourself about?

5. What can you do next month to consider yourself successful?

....
....
....
....
....
....
....
....
....
....
....
....
....
....
....
....
....
....
....
....
....

Tapping Into Other Artforms

Changing artistic mediums helps you to expand your creative mind and brings more depth to your work. Brainstorm how you can dabble in other artforms to enhance your main art. Don't worry about being "good," do it for fun inspiration.

Sketching or painting ....
....
....

Photography ....
....
....

Performance...
....
....

Writing or poetry ....
....
....

Design...
....
....

Music...
....
....

Dance..
....
....

Sculpture or pottery ....
....
....

Other...
....
....

Week 37

Inspiration

Focus word or phrase

I will use the outdoors to keep me inspired by

I will use music or art to keep me inspired by

What I'm reading

I want to emulate

Other creatives I will talk to this week

When I feel frustrated, I will

I won't give up when

Planned break

I will be brave when

I will be proud when

I will share my work on

Productivity

Big goal(s) for this week:

Priority Level (1-3):

....

....

....

	Actionable tasks:	When I Will Complete:	Completed?:
Monday:			
Tuesday:			
Wednesday:			
Thursday:			
Friday:			
Weekend:			

For next week: ....

....

....

....

Week 38

Inspiration

Focus word or phrase

I will use the outdoors to keep me inspired by

I will use music or art to keep me inspired by

What I'm reading

I want to emulate

Other creatives I will talk to this week

When I feel frustrated, I will

I won't give up when

Planned break

I will be brave when

I will be proud when

I will share my work on

Productivity

Big goal(s) for this week: Priority Level (1-3):

....

....

....

Week 38

Monday:	Actionable tasks:	When I Will Complete:	Completed?:

Tuesday:	Actionable tasks:	When I Will Complete:	Completed?:

Wednesday:	Actionable tasks:	When I Will Complete:	Completed?:

Thursday:	Actionable tasks:	When I Will Complete:	Completed?:

Friday:	Actionable tasks:	When I Will Complete:	Completed?:

Weekend:	Actionable tasks:	When I Will Complete:	Completed?:

For next week: ....

....

....

....

Week 39

Inspiration

Focus word or phrase

I will use the outdoors to keep me inspired by

I will use music or art to keep me inspired by

What I'm reading

I want to emulate

Other creatives I will talk to this week

When I feel frustrated, I will

I won't give up when

Planned break

I will be brave when

I will be proud when

I will share my work on

Productivity

Big goal(s) for this week:

Priority Level (1-3):

Week
39

....

....

....

	Actionable tasks:	When I Will Complete:	Completed?:
Monday:			
Tuesday:			
Wednesday:			
Thursday:			
Friday:			
Weekend:			

For next week: ....

....

....

....

Week 40

Inspiration

Focus word or phrase

I will use the outdoors to keep me inspired by

I will use music or art to keep me inspired by

What I'm reading

I want to emulate

Other creatives I will talk to this week

When I feel frustrated, I will

I won't give up when

Planned break

I will be brave when

I will be proud when

I will share my work on

Productivity

Big goal(s) for this week: Priority Level (1-3):

....

....

....

	Actionable tasks:	When I Will Complete:	Completed?:
Monday:			
Tuesday:			
Wednesday:			
Thursday:			
Friday:			
Weekend:			

For next week: ....

....

....

....

Monthly Reflections

1. Would you consider this month successful? Why or why not?
2. When were you at your best? Why do you think that is?
3. When were you at your least productive? Why?
4. Is there anything you are being too hard on yourself about?
5. What can you do next month to consider yourself successful?

....

....

....

....

....

....

....

....

....

....

....

....

....

....

....

....

....

....

....

....

....

....

....

Researching the Greats

Spend some time digging into the great artists of your medium, contemporary and classic. Think about what you would like to emulate in your work.

Name	My Favorites of Theirs	Their Style

Week

41

Inspiration

Focus word or phrase

I will use the outdoors
to keep me inspired by

I will use music or art
to keep me inspired by

What I'm reading

I want to emulate

Other creatives I will
talk to this week

When I feel frustrated,
I will

I won't give up when

Planned break

I will be brave when

I will be proud when

I will share my work on

Productivity

Big goal(s) for this week:

....
....
....

Priority Level (1-3):

Week 41

Monday:	Actionable tasks:	When I Will Complete:	Completed?:

Tuesday:	Actionable tasks:	When I Will Complete:	Completed?:

Wednesday:	Actionable tasks:	When I Will Complete:	Completed?:

Thursday:	Actionable tasks:	When I Will Complete:	Completed?:

Friday:	Actionable tasks:	When I Will Complete:	Completed?:

Weekend:	Actionable tasks:	When I Will Complete:	Completed?:

For next week: ....
....
....
....

Week 42

Inspiration

Focus word or phrase

I will use the outdoors to keep me inspired by

I will use music or art to keep me inspired by

What I'm reading

I want to emulate

Other creatives I will talk to this week

When I feel frustrated, I will

I won't give up when

Planned break

I will be brave when

I will be proud when

I will share my work on

Productivity

Big goal(s) for this week: Priority Level (1-3):

....

....

....

Week 42

	Actionable tasks:	When I Will Complete:	Completed?:
Monday:			
Tuesday:			
Wednesday:			
Thursday:			
Friday:			
Weekend:			

For next week: ....

....

....

....

Week 43

Inspiration

Focus word or phrase

I will use the outdoors to keep me inspired by

I will use music or art to keep me inspired by

What I'm reading

I want to emulate

Other creatives I will talk to this week

When I feel frustrated, I will

I won't give up when

Planned break

I will be brave when

I will be proud when

I will share my work on

Productivity

Big goal(s) for this week:

Priority Level (1-3):

....

....

....

Week 43

	Actionable tasks:	When I Will Complete:	Completed?:
Monday:			
Tuesday:			
Wednesday:			
Thursday:			
Friday:			
Weekend:			

For next week: ....

....

....

....

Week 44

Inspiration

Focus word or phrase

I will use the outdoors to keep me inspired by

I will use music or art to keep me inspired by

What I'm reading

I want to emulate

Other creatives I will talk to this week

When I feel frustrated, I will

I won't give up when

Planned break

I will be brave when

I will be proud when

I will share my work on

Productivity

Big goal(s) for this week: Priority Level (1-3):

....

....

....

	Actionable tasks:	When I Will Complete:	Completed?:
Monday:			
Tuesday:			
Wednesday:			
Thursday:			
Friday:			
Weekend:			

For next week: ....

....

....

....

Monthly Reflections

1. Would you consider this month successful? Why or why not?

2. When were you at your best? Why do you think that is?

3. When were you at your least productive? Why?

4. Is there anything you are being too hard on yourself about?

5. What can you do next month to consider yourself successful?

....
....
....
....
....
....
....
....
....
....
....
....
....
....
....
....
....
....
....
....
....
....

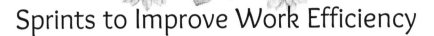

Sprints to Improve Work Efficiency

Being able to work efficiently is key to overall productivity. Sometimes we can get caught up in the process and spend to much time on details or waiting for perfection. Think of some sprint-style exercises you can incorporate this month that are only five minutes long and force you to think fast.

Sprint Activity	Results
....	....
....	....
....	....
....	....
....	....
....	....
....	....
....	....
....	....
....	....
....	....
....	....
....	....
....	....
....	....
....	....
....	....
....	....
....	....
....	....

Week
45

Inspiration

Focus word or phrase

I will use the outdoors to keep me inspired by

I will use music or art to keep me inspired by

What I'm reading

I want to emulate

Other creatives I will talk to this week

When I feel frustrated, I will

I won't give up when

Planned break

I will be brave when

I will be proud when

I will share my work on

Productivity

Big goal(s) for this week:

....
....
....

Priority Level (1-3):

Week 45

	Actionable tasks:	When I Will Complete:	Completed?:
Monday:			
Tuesday:			
Wednesday:			
Thursday:			
Friday:			
Weekend:			

For next week: ....
....
....
....

Week
46

Inspiration

Focus word or phrase

I will use the outdoors
to keep me inspired by

I will use music or art
to keep me inspired by

What I'm reading

I want to emulate

Other creatives I will
talk to this week

When I feel frustrated,
I will

I won't give up when

Planned break

I will be brave when

I will be proud when

I will share my work on

Productivity

Big goal(s) for this week:

Priority Level (1-3):

....

....

....

Week 46

	Actionable tasks:	When I Will Complete:	Completed?:
Monday:			
Tuesday:			
Wednesday:			
Thursday:			
Friday:			
Weekend:			

For next week: ....

....

....

....

Week
47

Inspiration

Focus word or phrase

I will use the outdoors to keep me inspired by

I will use music or art to keep me inspired by

What I'm reading

I want to emulate

Other creatives I will talk to this week

When I feel frustrated, I will

I won't give up when

Planned break

I will be brave when

I will be proud when

I will share my work on

Productivity

Big goal(s) for this week:

Priority Level (1-3):

....

....

....

	Actionable tasks:	When I Will Complete:	Completed?:
Monday:			
Tuesday:			
Wednesday:			
Thursday:			
Friday:			
Weekend:			

For next week: ....

....

....

....

Week 48

Inspiration

Focus word or phrase

I will use the outdoors to keep me inspired by

I will use music or art to keep me inspired by

What I'm reading

I want to emulate

Other creatives I will talk to this week

When I feel frustrated, I will

I won't give up when

Planned break

I will be brave when

I will be proud when

I will share my work on

Productivity

Big goal(s) for this week:　　　Priority Level (1-3):

....

....

....

Monday:	Actionable tasks:	When I Will Complete:	Completed?:

Tuesday:	Actionable tasks:	When I Will Complete:	Completed?:

Wednesday:	Actionable tasks:	When I Will Complete:	Completed?:

Thursday:	Actionable tasks:	When I Will Complete:	Completed?:

Friday:	Actionable tasks:	When I Will Complete:	Completed?:

Weekend:	Actionable tasks:	When I Will Complete:	Completed?:

For next week: ....

....

....

....

Monthly Reflections

1. Would you consider this month successful? Why or why not?

2. When were you at your best? Why do you think that is?

3. When were you at your least productive? Why?

4. Is there anything you are being too hard on yourself about?

5. What can you do next month to consider yourself successful?

Collaborating with Other Creatives

One of my favorite things as a writer is to work with illustrators. It brings a whole new dimension to my stories. Think of creatives in other mediums you know and something you could work on together, large or small.

Name	Craft	Collaboration Idea(s)

Week 49

Inspiration

Focus word or phrase

I will use the outdoors to keep me inspired by

I will use music or art to keep me inspired by

What I'm reading

I want to emulate

Other creatives I will talk to this week

When I feel frustrated, I will

I won't give up when

Planned break

I will be brave when

I will be proud when

I will share my work on

Productivity

Big goal(s) for this week:

....

....

....

Priority Level (1-3):

Week 49

	Actionable tasks:	When I Will Complete:	Completed?:
Monday:			
Tuesday:			
Wednesday:			
Thursday:			
Friday:			
Weekend:			

For next week: ....

....

....

....

Week
50

Inspiration

Focus word or phrase

I will use the outdoors to keep me inspired by

I will use music or art to keep me inspired by

What I'm reading

I want to emulate

Other creatives I will talk to this week

When I feel frustrated, I will

I won't give up when

Planned break

I will be brave when

I will be proud when

I will share my work on

Productivity

Big goal(s) for this week:

Priority Level (1-3):

....

....

....

Week 50

	Actionable tasks:	When I Will Complete:	Completed?:
Monday:			
Tuesday:			
Wednesday:			
Thursday:			
Friday:			
Weekend:			

For next week: ....

....

....

....

Week 51

Inspiration

Focus word or phrase

I will use the outdoors to keep me inspired by

I will use music or art to keep me inspired by

What I'm reading

I want to emulate

Other creatives I will talk to this week

When I feel frustrated, I will

I won't give up when

Planned break

I will be brave when

I will be proud when

I will share my work on

Productivity

Big goal(s) for this week:

Priority Level (1-3):

Week 51

....

....

....

	Actionable tasks:	When I Will Complete:	Completed?:
Monday:			
Tuesday:			
Wednesday:			
Thursday:			
Friday:			
Weekend:			

For next week: ....

....

....

....

Week

52

Inspiration

Focus word or phrase

I will use the outdoors to keep me inspired by

I will use music or art to keep me inspired by

What I'm reading

I want to emulate

Other creatives I will talk to this week

When I feel frustrated, I will

I won't give up when

Planned break

I will be brave when

I will be proud when

I will share my work on

Productivity

Big goal(s) for this week:

Priority Level (1-3):

....

....

....

Week 52

	Actionable tasks:	When I Will Complete:	Completed?:
Monday:			
Tuesday:			
Wednesday:			
Thursday:			
Friday:			
Weekend:			

For next week: ....

....

....

....

End-of-Year Reflection

You did it! You made it through the whole year!
Plan a celebration for yourself as a reward for
all of your hard work.

Look back at the big goals you made for the year in the beginning of this journal. How
did you do overall on achieving your goals?

....
....
....
....
....

What were the high points of your year? ....

....
....
....
....

The low points? ....

....
....
....
....

What activities from this journal made you feel the most inspired? ....

....
....
....
....

When were you the most productive? ....

....
....
....
....

Notes for Next Year

Shiny New Ideas

Shiny New Ideas

Shiny New Ideas

Shiny New Ideas

Did you enjoy this journal?

If you enjoyed this journal, please consider leaving a review on Amazon. It helps my small business to sell more books. Have suggestions? I would love to hear them. You can email me at **info@orangeblossombooks.com**.

Check out some of our other Focus Journals:

Mothers' Journal for Inner Peace
Quarantine Journal for Sanity
Teachers' Journal for Balance

www.orangeblossombooks.com

Made in the USA
Las Vegas, NV
26 February 2022

44655765R00085